D1173910

WITHDRAWN

AQUINAS COLLEGE LIBRARY
JUVENILE
Mother Goose rhymes
3 5060 00205 777 6

OLD DR. FOSTER

Old Dr. Foster
Went to Glo'ster
In a shower of rain;
He stepped in a puddle,
Up to the middle,
And never went there again.

GREAT "A", LITTLE "A"

Great "A", Little "A",
Bouncing "B".
The cat's in the cupboard,
And can't see me.

IS JOHN SMITH WITHIN?

Is John Smith within?
Yes, that he is,
Can he set a shoe?
Ay, marry, two.
Here a nail, there a prod
Now your horse is shod.

SEE A PIN AND PICK IT UP

See a pin and pick it up,
All the day you'll have good luck.
See a pin and let it **lay,**
Bad luck you'll have all the day.

SEE-SAW, SACARADOWN

See-saw, sacaradown,
Which is the way to London town?
One foot up, the other foot down,
Oh, that's the way to London town.

HEY! DIDDLE, DIDDLE!

Hey! diddle, diddle!
The cat and the fiddle,
The cow jumped over the moon;
The little dog laughed
To see such sport,
And the dish ran away with the
spoon.

BARBER, BARBER, SHAVE A PIG

Barber, barber, shave a pig,
How many hairs will make a wig?
"Four and twenty, that's enough."
Give the poor barber a pinch of
snuff.

LITTLE BETTY PRINGLE

Little Betty Pringle she had a pig.
It was not very little and not very
big;
When he was alive he lived in
clover,
But now he's dead, and that's all
over.

Johnny Pringle he sat down and
cry'd,
Betty Pringle she laid down and
dy'd;
So there was an end of one, two and
three;
Johnny Pringle he, Betty Pringle
she,
And Piggy Wiggie.

JACK AND JILL

Jack and Jill went up the hill
  To fetch a pail of water;
Jack fell down and broke his crown
  And Jill came tumbling after.

Up Jack got and home did trot
  As fast as he could caper;
Went to bed and bound his head
  With vinegar and brown paper.

When Jill came in how she did grin
  To see Jack's paper plaster;
Mother vexed, did whip her next
  For causing Jack's disaster.

COCK ROBIN GOT UP EARLY

Cock Robin got up early
  At the break of day,
And went to Jenny's window
  To sing a roundelay.

He sang Cock Robin's love
  To pretty Jenny Wren,
And when he got unto the end,
  Then he began again.

DOCTOR FAUSTUS

Doctor Faustus was a good man,
He whipped his scholars now and
  then;
When he whipped them he made
  them dance,
Out of Scotland into France.
Out of France into Spain,
And then he whipped them back
  again!

I WOULD IF I COULD

I would if I could
If I couldn't, how could I?
I couldn't, without I could, could I?
Could you, without you could,
  could you?
Could you, could you?
Could you, without you could,
  could you?

I SAW THREE SHIPS

I saw three ships come sailing by,
  Come sailing by, come sailing by;
I saw three ships come sailing by,
  On New Year's Day in the morn-
    ing.

And what do you think was in
    them then,
  Was in them then, was in them
    then?
And what do you think was in
    them then,
  On New Year's Day in the morn-
    ing?

Three pretty girls were in them
    then,
  Were in them then, were in them
    then;
Three pretty girls were in them
    then,
  On New Year's Day in the morn-
    ing.

One could whistle, and one could
  sing,
And one could play the violin,—
Such joy was there at my wedding,
On New Year's Day in the morn-
    ing.

SMILING GIRLS, ROSY BOYS

Smiling girls, rosy boys,
  Come and buy my little toys;
Monkeys made of ginger bread,
  And sugar horses painted red.

I HAD TWO PIGEONS

I had two pigeons bright and gay;
They flew from me the other day;
What was the reason they did go?
I cannot tell, for I do not know.

MULTIPLICATION IS VEXATION

Multiplication is vexation,
Division is as bad;
The Rule of Three doth puzzle me,
And Practice drives me mad.

OH, THAT I WAS WHERE I WOULD BE!

Oh, that I was where I would be!
Then would I be where I am not!
But where I am I must be,
And where I would be I cannot.

MONDAY ALONE

Monday alone, Tuesday together,
Wednesday we walk when it's fine weather.
Thursday we kiss, Friday we sigh
Saturday's hours seem almost to fly.
But of all days in the week we will call
Sunday, the rest day, the best day of all.

AS I WENT THROUGH THE GARDEN GAP

As I went through the garden gap!
Who should I meet but Dick Red-cap!
A stick in his hand, a stone in his throat.
If you'll tell me this riddle,
I'll give you a groat.

(A cherry)

OLD MOTHER TWITCHETT

Old Mother Twitchett had but one eye,
And a long tail which she let fly;
And every time she went through a gap
A bit of her tail she left in the trap.

(A needle)

PITTY PATTY POLT

Pitty Patty Polt,
Shoe the wild colt;
Here a nail,
And there a nail,
Pitty Patty Polt.

THE NORTH WIND DOTH BLOW

The north wind doth blow,
And we shall have snow,
And what will poor Robin do then?
Poor thing!

He'll sit in the barn,
And keep himself warm,
And hide his head under his wing.
Poor thing!

A DOG AND A CAT

A dog and a cat went out together,
To see some friends just out of the town;
Said the cat to the dog,
"What d'ye think of the weather?
"I think, ma'am, the rain will come down—
But don't be alarmed, for I've an umbrella
That will shelter us both," said this amiable fellow.

ROBIN HOOD

Robin Hood, Robin Hood
Is in the mickle wood!
Little John, Little John,
He to the town is gone.

Robin Hood, Robin Hood
Is telling his beads,
All in the greenwood,
Among the green weeds.

Little John, Little John,
If he comes no more,
Robin Hood, Robin Hood,
He will fret full sore!

ROBIN THE BOBBIN

Robin the Bobbin, the big-belted
Ben,
He ate more meat than fourscore
men;
He ate a cow, he ate a calf,
He ate a butcher and a half,
He ate a church, he ate a steeple,
He ate the priest and all the
people!
A cow and a calf,
An ox and a half,
A church and a steeple,
And all the good people,
And yet he complained that his
stomach wasn't full.

BAA, BAA, BLACK SHEEP

Baa, baa, black sheep,
Have you any wool?
Yes, sir, yes, sir,
Three bags full:
One for my master,
One for my dame,
But none for the little boy
Who cries in the lane.

WHEN I WAS A LITTLE GIRL

When I was a little girl, I washed
my mammy's dishes:
Now I am a big girl, I roll in golden
riches.

THE WINDS THEY DID BLOW

The winds they did blow,
The leaves they did wag;
Along came a beggar-boy,
And put me in his bag.

He took me up to London,
A lady did me buy;
Put me in a silver cage,
And hung me up on high.

With apples by the fire,
And nuts for to crack;
Besides a little feather-bed,
To rest my little back.
(A squirrel)

A JOLLY OLD PIG

A jolly old pig once lived in a
sty,
And three little piggies had
she,
And she waddled about saying
"Grumph! grumph! grumph!"
While the little ones said "Wee!
wee!"
And she waddled about saying
"Grumph! grumph! grumph!"
While the little ones said "Wee!
wee!"

HUSH-A-BY, BABY

Hush-a-by, baby, lie still in the
cradle,
Mother has gone to buy a soup
ladle;
When she comes back she'll bring
us some meat,
And father and baby shall have
some to eat.

BURNIE BEE, BURNIE BEE

Burnie bee, burnie bee,
Say, when will your wedding be?
If it be to-morrow day,
Take your wings and fly away.

AN APPLE PIE

An apple pie, when it looks nice,
Would make one long to have a
  slice;
And if the taste should prove so,
  too,
I fear one slice would hardly do.
So to prevent my asking twice,
Pray, mamma, cut a good large
  slice.

TOMMY TROT

Tommy Trot, a man of law,
Sold his bed and lay upon straw;
Sold the straw, and slept on grass,
To buy his wife a looking-glass.

A MAN WENT A-HUNTING AT REIGATE

A man went a-hunting at Reigate,
And wished to leap over a high
  gate.
Says the owner, "Go round,
With your dog and your hound,
For you never shall leap over my
  gate."

A LITTLE BOY

A little boy went into a barn,
  And lay down on some hay;
An owl came out and flew about,
  And the little boy ran away.

IF ALL THE WORLD WAS APPLE-PIE

If all the world was apple-pie
  And all the sea was ink,
And all the trees were bread and
  cheese,
  What should we have to drink?
It's enough to make an old man
  Scratch his head and think.

PIT, PAT, WELL-A-DAY

Pit, pat, well-a-day,
Little Robin flew away.
Where can little Robin be?
Gone into the cherry tree.

THERE WAS A LITTLE GREEN HOUSE

There was a little green house
And in the little green house
There was a little brown house,
And in the little brown house
There was a little yellow house,
And in the little yellow house
There was a little white house,
And in the little white house,
There was a little heart.
(A walnut)

LITTLE JUMPING JOAN

Here am I, little jumping Joan,
When nobody's with me
I'm always alone.

ONE MISTY MOISTY MORNING

One misty moisty morning,
When cloudy was the weather,
I chanced to meet an old man
Clothed all in leather.

He began to compliment
And I began to grin,
With " How do you do," and "How
do you do,"
And "How do you do again?"

SHOE THE HORSE

Shoe the horse, and shoe the mare
But let the little colt go bare.

BYE, BABY BUNTING

Bye, baby bunting,
Daddy's gone a-hunting,
To get a little rabbit's skin,
To wrap a baby bunting in.

FOREHEAD, EYES, CHEEKS, NOSE, MOUTH, AND CHIN

Here sits the Lord Mayor,
Here sits his two men,
Here sits the cock,
Here sits the hen,
Here sit the little chickens,
Here they run in.
Chin-chopper, chin-chopper,
chin-chopper, chin!

THIS IS THE WAY THE LADIES RIDE

This is the way the ladies ride;
Tri, tre, tre, tree,
Tri, tre, tre, tree!
This is the way the ladies ride,
Tri, tre, tre, tre, tri, tre, tre, tree!

This is the way the gentlemen ride;
Gallop-a-trot,
Gallop-a-trot!
This is the way the gentlemen ride,
Gallop-a-trot-a-trot.

This is the way the farmers ride;
Hobbledy-hoy,
Hobbledy-hoy!
This is the way the farmers ride,
Hobbledy-hobbledy-hoy!

SNEEZE ON MONDAY

Sneeze on Monday, sneeze for danger;
Sneeze on Tuesday, kiss a stranger;
Sneeze on Wednesday, get a letter;
Sneeze on Thursday, something better;
Sneeze on Friday, sneeze for sorrow;
Sneeze on Saturday, see your sweetheart to-morrow.

THE MILLER HE GRINDS HIS CORN

The miller he grinds his corn, his corn;
The miller he grinds his corn, his corn;
The Little Boy Blue comes blowing his horn,
With a hop, step, and a jump.

YOU RIDE BEHIND

You ride behind and I'll ride before,
And trot, trot away to Baltimore.
You shall take bread and I will take honey,
And both of us carry a purse full of money.

I SAW A SHIP A-SAILING

I saw a ship a-sailing,
A-sailing on the sea;
And, oh! it was all laden
With pretty things for thee!

There were comfits in the cabin,
And apples in the hold;
The sails were made of silk,
And the masts were made of gold.

The four-and-twenty sailors
That stood between the decks,
Were four-and-twenty white mice,
With chains about their necks.

The captain was a duck,
With a packet on his back;
And when the ship began to move,
The captain said, "Quack! quack!"

THERE WAS A LITTLE BOY AND A LITTLE GIRL

There was a little boy and a little girl
Lived in an alley;
Says the little boy to the little girl,
"Shall I, oh! shall I?"

Says the little girl to the little boy,
"What shall we do?"
Says the little boy to the little girl,
"I will kiss you."

CACKLE, CACKLE

Cackle, cackle, Madam Goose!
Have you any feathers loose?
Truly have I, little fellow,
Half enough to fill a pillow;
And here are quills, take one or ten,
And make from each popgun or pen.

HICK-A-MORE, HACK-A-MORE

Hick-a-more, Hack-a-more,
On the King's kitchen door;
All the King's horses,
And all the King's men
Couldn't drive Hick-a-more, Hack-a-more
Off the King's kitchen door!
(Sunshine)

COME, LET'S TO BED

Come, let's to bed,
Says Sleepy-head;
Tarry awhile, says Slow;
Put on the pan,
Says Greedy Nan,
Let's sup before we go.

INTERY, MINTERY, CUTERY, CORN

Intery, mintery, cutery, corn,
Apple seed and apple thorn;
Wire, brier, limber lock,
Three geese in a flock,
One flew east, one flew west,
And one flew over the goose's nest.

CROSS PATCH

Cross patch
Draw the latch,
Sit by the fire and spin;
Take a cup
And drink it up,
Then call your neighbors in.

DOODLE DOODLE DOO

Doodle Doodle doo,
The Princess lost her shoe;
Her Highness hopped,—
The fiddler stopped,
Not knowing what to do.

SING, SING! WHAT SHALL I SING?

Sing, sing! what shall I sing?
The cat has eaten the pudding-string!
Do, do! What shall I do?
The cat has bitten it quite in two.

I AM A GOLD KEY

I am a gold lock.
I am a gold key.
I am a silver lock.
I am a silver key.
I am a brass lock.
I am a brass key.
I am a lead lock.
I am a lead key.
I am a monk lock.
I am a monk key!

ONE TO MAKE READY

One to make ready,
And two to prepare;
Good luck to the rider,
And away goes the mare.

DEAR, DEAR!

Dear, dear! what can the matter be?
Two old women got up in an apple-tree;
One came down, and the other stayed till Saturday.

THE OLD WOMAN

The old woman must stand at the tub, tub, tub,
The dirty clothes to rub, rub, rub;
But when they are clean and fit to be seen,
I'll dress like a lady, and dance on the green.

LUCY LOCKET

Lucy Locket
Lost her pocket,
Kitty Fisher found it;
Nothing in it,
Nothing in it,
But the binding round it.

HANDY-SPANDY

Handy-Spandy, Jack-a-dandy,
Loved plum-cake and sugar-candy.
He bought some at a grocer's shop,
And out he came, hop, hop, hop.

MY LITTLE OLD MAN AND I FELL OUT

My little old man and I fell out,
I'll tell you what 't was all about;
I had money and he had none,
And that's the way the row begun.

TOM, TOM, THE PIPER'S SON

Tom, Tom, the piper's son,
Stole a pig and away did run!
The pig was eat, and Tom was beat,
Till he ran crying down the street.

MATTHEW, MARK, LUKE AND JOHN

Matthew, Mark, Luke and John,
Bless the bed that I lie on!
All the four corners round about,
When I get in, when I get out.

Four corners to my bed,
Four angels round my head;
One to watch and one to pray,
And two to bear my soul away.

THERE WAS AN OLD WOMAN

There was an old woman,
And nothing she had;
And so this old woman
Was said to be mad.
She'd nothing to eat,
She'd nothing to wear,
She'd nothing to lose,
She'd nothing to fear,
She'd nothing to ask,
And nothing to give,
And when she did die,
She'd nothing to leave.

TO MARKET, TO MARKET

To market, to market, to buy a fat pig,
Home again, home again, jiggety jig;
To market, to market, to buy a fat hog,
Home again, home again, jiggety jog.

To market, to market, to buy a plum bun,
Home again, home again, market is done;
To market, to market, to buy a plum cake,
Home again, home again, ne'er a one baked,—
The baker is dead, and all his men,
And we must go to market again.

THERE WAS A JOLLY MILLER

There was a jolly miller
Lived on the river Dee;
He worked and sang from morn till night,
No lark as blithe as he.

And as the burden of his song
For ever used to be:
"I care for nobody—no! not I,
Since nobody cares for me."

I HAD A LITTLE DOG

I had a little dog, and his name
was Blue Bell,
I gave him some work, and he did
it very well;
I sent him upstairs to pick up a pin,
He stepped in the coal-scuttle up
to his chin.

RIDDLE-ME, RIDDLE-ME, RIDDLE-ME-REE

Riddle-Me, riddle-me, riddle-me-
ree,
Perhaps you can tell what this
riddle may be:
As deep as a house, as round as a
cup,
And all the King's horses can't
draw it up.

(A well)

TWO ROBIN REDBREASTS

Two Robin Redbreasts built their
nest
Within a hollow tree;
The hen sat quietly at home,
The cock sang merrily;
And all the little young ones said,
"Wee, wee, wee, wee, wee, wee."

One day the sun was warm and
bright,
And shining in the sky,
Cock Robin said, "My little dears,
'Tis time you learn to fly."
And all the little young ones said,
"I'll try, I'll try, I'll try."

I know a child, and who she is
I'll tell you by and by,
When mamma says, "Do this," or
"that,"
She says, "What for?" and "Why?"
She'd be a better child by far
If she would say, "I'll try."

BAT, BAT, COME UNDER MY HAT

Bat, bat, come under my hat,
And I'll give you a slice of bacon;
And when I bake, I'll give you a
cake,
If I am not mistaken.

MARY HAD A LITTLE LAMB

Mary had a little lamb,
  Its fleece was white as snow;
And everywhere that Mary went
  The lamb was sure to go.

It followed her to school one day,
  That was against the rule;
It made the children laugh and
    play,
  To see a lamb at school.

And so the teacher turned it out,
  But still it lingered near;
And waited patiently about
  Till Mary did appear.

"Why does the lamb love Mary
    so?"
  The eager children cry;
"Why, Mary loves the lamb, you
    know!"
  The teacher did reply.

WHAT SHOEMAKER?

What shoemaker makes shoes
  without leather,
With all the four elements put
  together?
Fire and water, earth and air;
Every customer has two pair.
(A horse-shoer)

THE SPIDER AND THE FLY

"Will you walk into my parlor?"
  Said the spider to the fly;
" 'Tis the prettiest little parlor
  That ever you did spy.

The way into my parlor
  Is up a winding stair;
And I have many curious things
  To show you when you're there."

"Oh, no, no," said the little fly;
  "To ask me is in vain;
For who goes up your winding
    stair
  Can ne'er come down again."

JACK JELF

Little Jack Jelf
Was put on the shelf
Because he could not spell "pie;"
When his aunt, Mrs. Grace,
Saw his sorrowful face,
She could not help saying, "Oh,
fie!"

And since Master Jelf
Was put on the shelf
Because he could not spell "pie,"
Let him stand there so grim,
And no more about him,
For I wish him a very good-bye!

SIMPLE SIMON

Simple Simon met a pieman
Going to the fair;
Says Simple Simon to the pieman,
"Let me taste your ware."

Says the pieman to Simple Simon,
"Show me first your penny";
Says Simple Simon to the pieman,
"Indeed, I have not any."

Simple Simon went a-fishing
For to catch a whale;
All the water he could find
Was in his mother's pail!

Simple Simon went to look
If plums grew on a thistle;
He pricked his fingers very much,
Which made poor Simon whistle.

He went to catch a dicky bird,
And thought he could not fail,
Because he had a little salt,
To put upon its tail.

He went for water with a sieve,
But soon it ran all through;
And now poor Simple Simon
Bids you all adieu.

FEARS AND TEARS

Tommy's tears and Mary's fears
Will make them old before their
years.

WHEN LITTLE FRED WENT TO BED

When little Fred went to bed,
He always said his prayers;
He kissed mamma, and then papa,
And straightway went upstairs.

THE KING OF IAN

The King of Ian was very fat,
Had a crown, but not a hat;
Oh, what a king was that, was that!
Oh rat, tat tat; oh rat, tat, tat.

ONE, TWO, THREE, FOUR

One, two, three, four,
Mary at the cottage door;
Five, six, seven, eight,
Eating berries off a plate;
O-U-T spells out!

RUB-A-DUB-DUB

Rub-a-dub-dub,—
Three men in a tub,
And who do you think they be?
The butcher, the baker,
The candle-stick maker,
Turn 'em out, knaves all three.

THIS LITTLE PIG WENT TO MARKET

This little pig went to market;
This little pig stayed at home;
This little pig had roast beef,
This little pig had none;
This little pig said, "Wee, Wee!
I can't find my way home."

BILLY, BILLY, COME AND PLAY

"Billy, Billy, come and play,
While the sun shines bright as
day."
"Yes, my Polly, so I will,
For I love to please you still."

"Billy, Billy, have you seen
Sam and Betsy on the green?"
"Yes, my Polly, I saw them pass,
Skipping over the new-mown
grass."

"Billy, Billy, come along,
And I will sing a pretty song."
"Oh, then, Polly, I'll make haste,
Not one moment will I waste,
But will come and hear you sing,
And my fiddle I will bring."

I WENT UP ONE PAIR OF STAIRS

"I went up one pair of stairs."
"Just like me."
"I went up two pair of stairs."
"Just like me."
"I went into a room."
"Just like me."
"I looked out a window."
"Just like me."
"And there I saw a monkey."
"Just like me!!!"

AS SOON AS I COULD BAIT MY HOOK

As soon as I could bait my hook,
I dropped the line into the brook,
A trout soon saw and quickly
caught it;
I pulled, and pulled, and out I
brought it;
My first brook trout!
I then was small,
But felt that instant six feet tall.

LITTLE TEE WEE

Little Tee Wee,
He went to sea
In an open boat;
And while afloat
The little boat bended,
And my story's ended.

I HAD A LITTLE HOBBY-HORSE

I had a little hobby-horse,
And it was dapple gray,
Its head was made of pea-straw,
Its tail was made of hay.
I sold it to an old woman
For a copper groat;
And I'll not sing my song again
Without a new coat.

A LITTLE OLD MAN AND I FELL OUT

A little old man and I fell out,
How shall we bring the matter about?
Bring it about as well as you can,
Get you gone, you little old man!

SING A SONG OF SIXPENCE

Sing a song of sixpence,
A pocket full of rye;
Four and twenty blackbirds
Baked in a pie.
When the pie was opened,
The birds began to sing;
Was not that a dainty dish
To set before the king?

The king was in his counting-house
Counting out his money;
The queen was in the parlor
Eating bread and honey;
The maid was in the garden
Hanging out the clothes,
There came a little blackbird,
And snapped off her nose.

THE ROBIN AND THE REDBREAST

The robin and the redbreast,
The robin and the wren—
If you take out of their nest,
You'll never thrive again.

The robin and the redbreast,
The martin and the swallow—
If you touch one of their eggs,
Bad luck is sure to follow.

DICKERY, DICKERY DOCK

Dickery, dickery, dock!
The mouse ran up the clock;
The clock struck one, and down he ran;
Dickery, dickery, dock!

LITTLE ROBIN REDBREAST SAT UPON A TREE

Little Robin Redbreast sat upon a tree,
Up went Pussy cat, and down went he;
Down came Pussy cat, and away Robin ran;
Says little Robin Redbreast, "Catch me if you can."

Little Robin Redbreast jumped upon a wall,
Pussy cat jumped after him, and almost got a fall.
Little Robin chirped and sang, and what did Pussy say?
Pussy cat said, "Mew," and Robin jumped away.

A LITTLE COCK SPARROW

A little cock sparrow sat on a green tree,
And he chirruped, he chirruped, so merry was he.

A little cock sparrow sat on a green tree,
And he chirruped, he chirruped, so merry was he.

UP IN THE GREEN ORCHARD

Up in the green orchard there is a green tree,
The finest of pippins that ever you see;

The apples are ripe and ready to fall,
And Bobby and Johnny shall gather them all.

WEE WILLIE WINKIE

Wee Willie Winkie runs through the town,
Upstairs and downstairs in his night-gown,

Rapping at the window, crying through the lock
"Are the children all in bed for it's now eight o'clock?"

WHAT ARE LITTLE BOYS MADE OF?

What are little boys made of, made of?
What are little boys made of?
Frogs and snails, and puppy-dogs' tails;
And that's what little boys are made of, made of.

What are little girls made of, made of?
What are little girls made of?
Sugar and spice, and all that's nice;
And that's what little girls are made of, made of.

BOSSY-COW, BOSSY-COW

Bossy-cow, bossy-cow, where do you lie?
In the green meadow under the sky.

Billy-horse, billy-horse, where do you lie?
Out in the stable with nobody nigh.

Birdies bright, birdies sweet, where do you lie?
Up in the tree-tops,—oh, ever so high!

Baby dear, baby love, where do you lie?
In my warm crib, with Mamma close by.

A CAT CAME FIDDLING

A cat came fiddling out of a barn,
With a pair of bag-pipes under her arm:
She could sing nothing but fiddle cum fee,
The mouse has married the humble-bee;
Pipe, cat,—dance, mouse,
We'll have a wedding at our fine house.

THE MULBERRY BUSH

Here we go round the mulberry bush,
The mulberry bush, the mulberry bush,
Here we go round the mulberry bush,
On a cold and frosty morning.

This is the way we wash our hands,
Wash our hands, wash our hands,
This is the way we wash our hands,
On a cold and frosty morning.

This is the way we wash our clothes,
Wash our clothes, wash our clothes,
This is the way we wash our clothes,
On a cold and frosty morning.

This is the way we go to school,
Go to school, go to school,
This is the way we go to school,
On a cold and frosty morning.

This is the way we come out of school,
Come out of school, come out of school,
This is the way we come out of school,
On a cold and frosty morning.

SOME LITTLE MICE

Some little mice sat in a barn to spin,
When Pussy came by and popped her head in.
"Shall I come in and cut your threads off?"
"Oh no, Mrs. Pussy, you will snap our heads off!"

THERE WAS AN OLD CROW

There was an old crow
Sat upon a clod.
There's an end of my song,
That's very odd.

THERE WAS AN OLD WOMAN

There was an old woman tossed up in a basket,
Seventeen times as high as the moon;
And where she was going, I couldn't but ask it,
For in her hand she carried a broom.

"Old woman, old woman, old old woman," said I,
"O whither, O whither, O whither so high?"
"To sweep the cobwebs off the sky!"
"Shall I go with you?" "Aye, by-and-by."

FOUR AND TWENTY TAILORS

Four and twenty tailors
Went to kill a snail;
The best man amongst them
Durst not touch her tail.
She put out her horns,
Like a little Keyloe cow;
Run, tailors, run,
You're in dreadful danger now.

A MAN OF WORDS

A man of words and not of deeds,
Is like a garden full of weeds;
For when the weeds begin to grow,
Then doth the garden overflow.

FOR WANT OF A NAIL

For want of a nail, the shoe was
lost,
For want of the shoe, the horse was
lost,
For want of the horse, the rider was
lost,
For want of the rider, the battle
was lost,
For want of the battle, the kingdom
was lost,
And all for the want of a horseshoe
nail!

PRETTY PUSS

Come, pretty Cat!
Come here to me!
I want to pat
You on my knee.
Go, naughty Tray!
By barking thus,
You'll drive away
My pretty Puss.

FIRE, FIRE

"Fire! fire!" said the town crier;
"Where? where?" said Goody
Blair;
"Down the town," said Goody
Brown;
"I'll go and see it," said Goody
Fleet;
"So will I," said Goody Fry.

LOOBY, LOO

Here we dance Looby Loo,
Here we dance Looby Light,
Here we dance Looby Loo,
Dance with all your might.

Put your right hand in—and your
right hand out,
Shake yourself a little, and turn
yourself about.

LITTLE ROBIN REDBREAST

Little Robin Redbreast sat upon a
rail,
Niddle naddle went his head,
wiggle waggle went his tail.
Little Robin Redbreast sat upon a
hurdle,
With a pair of speckled legs and a
green girdle.

ROBERT BARNES, FELLOW FINE

"Robert Barnes, fellow fine,
Can you shoe this horse of mine?"
"Yes, good Sir, that I can,
As well as any other man;
There's a nail, and there's a prod,
And now, good Sir, your horse is shod."

EVENING RED

Evening red and morning gray,
Will set the traveler on his way;
But evening gray and morning red,
Will bring down rain upon his head.

THE ROBINS

A robin and a robin's son
Once went to town to buy a bun.
They couldn't decide on plum or plain,
And so they went back home again.

THE FAT MAN OF BOMBAY

There was a fat man of Bombay,
Who was smoking one sunshiny day,
When a bird, called a snipe,
Flew away with his pipe,
Which vexed the fat man of Bombay.

THE BUNCH OF BLUE RIBBONS

Oh, dear, what can the matter be?
Oh, dear, what can the matter be?
Oh, dear, what can the matter be?
Johnny's so long at the fair.

He promised he'd buy me a bunch of blue ribbons,
He promised he'd buy me a bunch of blue ribbons,
He promised he'd buy me a bunch of blue ribbons,
To tie up my bonny brown hair.

LITTLE QUEEN PIPPIN

Little Queen Pippin once built a hotel.
How long and how high, I'm sure I cannot tell;
The walls were of sugar, as white as the snow,
And beautiful windows were placed in a row;
The columns were candy, and all very tall,
And a roof of choice cakes was spread over all.

IF I HAD AS MUCH MONEY AS I COULD SPEND

If I had as much money as I could spend,
I never would cry old chairs to mend;
Old chairs to mend, old chairs to mend,
I never would cry old chairs to mend.

If I had as much money as I could tell,
I never would cry young lambs to sell,
Young lambs to sell, young lambs to sell,
I never would cry young lambs to sell.

FIDDLE-DE-DEE

Fiddle-de-dee, fiddle-de-dee,
The fly shall marry the bumble-bee.
They went to the church, and married was she,
The fly has married the bumble-bee.

GEORGIE PORGIE

Georgie Porgie, pudding and pie,
Kissed the girls and made them cry;
When the boys came out to play,
Georgie Porgie ran away.

POLLY-GALLENA

Polly-gallena, my fat hen,
Laid ivory eggs a score and ten;
Many good people call every day,
To look at the eggs my hen doth lay.

WHEN JACKY'S A VERY GOOD BOY

When Jacky's a very good boy,
He shall have cakes and a custard,
But when he does nothing but cry,
He shall have nothing but mustard.

DAME TROT AND HER CAT

Dame Trot and her cat
Led a peaceable life,
When they were not troubled
With other folks' strife.

When Dame had her dinner
Pussy would wait,
And was sure to receive
A nice piece from her plate.

SUKEY, YOU SHALL BE MY WIFE

Sukey, you shall be my wife,
And I will tell you why:
I have got a little pig,
And you have got a sty;
I have got a brown cow,
And you can make good cheese,
Sukey, will you have me?
Say yes, if you please.

LITTLE TOM TUCKER

Little Tom Tucker,
Sings for his supper;
What shall he eat?
White bread and butter;
How will he cut it
Without a knife?
How will he be married
Without a wife?

LITTLE STAR THAT SHINES SO BRIGHT

Little star that shines so bright,
Come and peep at me tonight,
For I often watch for you
In the pretty sky so blue.

Little star! O tell me, pray,
Where you hide yourself all day?
Have you got a home like me,
And a father kind to see?

Little Child, at you I peep
While you lie so fast asleep;
But when morn begins to break,
I my homeward journey take.

For I've many friends on high,
Living with me in the sky;
And a loving Father, too,
Who commands what I'm to do.

LITTLE FOLKS

Little folks, little folks,
Now then for bed!
A pillow is waiting
For each little head.

Sleep all the night,
And wake in the morn;
Robert shall sound
The call on his horn.

THE PUSSYCAT MEW

The Pussycat Mew jumped over a
coal,
And in her best petticoat burnt a
great hole.

Poor Pussy's weeping she'll have
no more milk,
Until her best petticoat's mended
with silk!

RIDE AWAY, RIDE AWAY

Ride away, ride away, Donald
  shall ride,
Ride to the city to get him a bride;

She shall be gentle, she shall be
  fair,
With gems on her fingers, and
  plumes in her hair.

LILIES ARE WHITE

Lilies are white,
Rosemary's green;
When you are king,
I will be queen.

Roses are red,
Lavender's blue;
If you will have me,
I will have you.

COME WHEN YOU ARE CALLED

Where's Susan, and Kitty, and
  Jane?
Where's Billy, and Sammy, and
  Jack?
O! there they are, down in the
  lane,
Go, Betty, and bring them all
  back.

But Billy is rude and won't come,
And Sammy is running too fast;
Come, dear little children, come
  home,
And Billy is coming at last.

I'm glad he remembers what's
  right,
For though he likes sliding on
  ice,
He should not be long out of sight,
And never want sending for
  twice.

JACK SPRAT'S PIG

Jack Sprat's pig,
He was not very little,
Nor yet very big;
He was not very lean,
He was not very fat;
He'll do well for a grunt,
Says little Jack Sprat.

LITTLE BO PEEP

RIDDLE-ME, RIDDLE-ME, REE

Riddle-me, riddle-me, ree,
A hawk sat up on a tree;
And he says to himself, says he,
Oh dear what a fine bird I be!

SPEAK KINDLY

Speak kindly to your dog, my boy!
All things that live know pain and
joy.
Speak harshly to your dog and see
How sad and shamed he seems to
be;
His head, and ears, and tail all say,
Oh! let me go far, far away!

LITTLE TOMMY TITTLE-MOUSE

Little Tommy Tittlemouse
Lived in a little house.
He caught fishes
In other men's ditches.

SEE, SEE! WHAT SHALL I SEE?

See, see! what shall I see?
A horse's head where his tail
should be.

LITTLE BO-PEEP

Little Bo-Peep has lost her sheep,
And can't tell where to find
them;
Leave them alone, and they'll
come home,
And bring their tails behind
them.

Little Bo-Peep fell fast asleep,
And dreamt she heard them
bleating;
But when she awoke, she found it
a joke,
For they still were all fleeting.

Then up she took her little crook,
Determined for to find them;
What was her joy to behold them
nigh,
Wagging their tails behind them.

LOOK AT MY DOG

Look at my dog. I call him Pink
Now sit up, Pink, and do not
  wink,
Look in my eyes! Steady, steady!

Hear the command! Are you ready?
Now, sir, attend! When I say four,
You'll walk three steps, and shut
  the door!

I HAD A LITTLE DOGGIE

I had a little doggie
  That used to sit and beg,
But Doggie tumbled down stairs,
  And broke his little leg.

Oh! Doggie, I will nurse you,
  And try to make you well;
And you shall have a collar
  With a pretty little bell.

Ah! Doggie, don't you think
  You should very faithful be,
For having such a loving friend
  To comfort you as me?

And when your leg is better,
  And you can run and play,
We'll have a scamper in the fields
  And see them making hay.

BOBBY SNOOKS

Little Bobby Snooks was fond of
  his books,
And loved by his usher and master;

But naughty Jack Spry, he got a
  black eye,
And carries his nose in a plaster.

THERE WAS AN OLD WOMAN OF NORWICH

There was an old woman of Norwich,
Who lived upon nothing but porridge;
Parading the town,
She turned cloak into gown,
This thrifty old woman of Norwich.

THE KING OF FRANCE

The King of France went up the hill
With twenty thousand men;
The King of France came down the hill,
And ne'er went up again.

HECTOR PROTECTOR

Hector Protector was dressed all in green;
Hector Protector was sent to the Queen.
The Queen did not like him,
No more did the King;
So Hector Protector was sent back again.

THERE WERE TWO BLACKBIRDS

There were two blackbirds sat upon a hill,
The one named Jack, the other named Jill.
Fly away, Jack, fly away, Jill;
Come again, Jack, come again, Jill.

THERE WERE TWO BIRDS

There were two birds sat on a stone,
Fa, la, la, la, lal, de;
One flew away and then there was one,
Fa, la, la, la, lal, de;
The other flew after and then there was none,
Fa, la, la, la, lal, de;
And so the poor stone was left all alone,
Fa, la, la, la, lal, de.

LITTLE MISS MUFFET

ONE, TWO, BUCKLE MY SHOE

One, two,
Buckle my shoe;

Three, four,
Shut the door;

Five, six,
Pick up sticks;

Seven, eight,
Lay them straight;

Nine, ten,
A good fat hen;

Eleven, twelve,
Who will delve?

Thirteen, fourteen,
Maids a-courting;

Fifteen, sixteen,
Maids a-kissing;

Seventeen, eighteen,
Maids a-waiting;

Nineteen, twenty,
My plate's empty.

LITTLE MISS MUFFET

Little Miss Muffet,
She sat on a tuffet,
Eating of curds and whey;
There came a big spider,
And sat down beside her,
And frightened Miss Muffet away.

OLD MOTHER GOOSE

Old Mother Goose when
She wanted to wander,
Would ride through the air
On a very fine gander.

Mother Goose had a house,
'Twas built in a wood,
Where an owl at the door
For a sentinel stood.

She had a son Jack,
A plain-looking lad,
He was not very good
Nor yet very bad.

COME, MY CHILDREN, COME AWAY

Come, my children, come away,
For the sun shines bright today;
Little children, come with me,
Birds and brooks and posies
  see;
Get your hats and come away,
For it is a pleasant day.

Everything is laughing, singing,
All the pretty flowers are spring-
  ing;
See the kitten, full of fun,
Sporting in the brilliant sun;
Children too may sport and play,
For it is a pleasant day.

HUSH, BABY, MY DOLL

Hush, baby, my doll, I pray you,
  don't cry,
And I'll give you some bread, and
  some milk by and by;

Or perhaps you like custard, or
  maybe a tart,
Then to either you are welcome,
  with all my heart.

TIT-TAT-TOE

Tit-tat-toe,
My first go,
Three jolly butcher boys
All in a row;
Stick one up, stick one down,
Stick one in the old man's crown!

Eggs,
butter,
bread,
Stick, stock, stone dead!
Stick him up, stick him down,
Stick him in the old man's crown!

I HAD A LITTLE PONY

I had a little pony,
  They called him Dapple-gray;
I lent him to a lady,
  To ride a mile away.

She whipped him, she slashed him,
  She rode him through the mire;
I would not lend my pony now,
  For all the lady's hire.

THE FIVE TOES

1. "Let us go to the woods," says this pig;
2. "What to do there?" says that pig;
3. "To look for mother," says this pig;
4. "What to do with her?" says that pig;
5. "To kiss her, to kiss her," says this pig.

RAIN, RAIN, GO AWAY

Rain, rain, go away,
Come again another day;
Little Johnny wants to play.

FOR EVERY EVIL UNDER THE SUN

For every evil under the sun,
There is a remedy, or there is none,
If there be one, seek till you find it;
If there be none, never mind it.

A LITTLE GREEN BIRD

A little green bird sat on a fence-rail,
  Chee-choo, chee-choo, chee.
It's song was the sweetest that I ever heard,
  Chee-choo, chee-choo, chee.

I ran for some salt to put on it's tail,
  Chee-choo, chee-choo, chee.
But while I was gone, away flew the bird,
  Chee-choo, chee-choo, chee.

WINTER SUN, SHINE OUT TODAY

Winter sun, shine out today,
For I'm to ride in Uncle's sleigh.

DICKERY, DICKERY, DARE

Dickery, dickery, dare,
The pig flew up in the air;
The man in brown soon brought him down,
Dickery, dickery, dare.

PUSSY-CAT, PUSSY-CAT

Pussy-cat, pussy-cat, where have you been?
I've been to London to look at the Queen.
Pussy-cat, pussy-cat, what did you there?
I frightened a little mouse under the chair.

MARY HAD A PRETTY BIRD

Mary had a pretty bird,
Feathers bright and yellow,
Slender legs—upon my word,
He was a pretty fellow.

COBBLER, COBBLER, MEND MY SHOE

Cobbler, cobbler, mend my shoe,
And get it done by half-past two:
If half-past two can't be done,
Get it done by half-past one.

Cobbler, cobbler, mend my shoe,
Give it a stitch and that will do:
Here's a nail and there's a prod,
And now my shoe is well shod.

ELIZABETH

Elizabeth, Elspeth, Betsy, and Bess,
They all went together to seek a bird's nest;
They found a bird's nest with five eggs in,
They all took one, and left four in.

THERE WAS AN OLD MAN OF TOBAGO

There was an old man of Tobago,
Who lived on rice, gruel, and sago;
Till, much to his bliss,
His physician said this—
"To a leg, sir, of mutton you may go."

LONDON BRIDGE IS FALLING DOWN

London Bridge is falling down,
Falling down, falling down;
London Bridge is falling down,
My fair lady.

You stole my watch and kept my keys,
Kept my keys, kept my keys;
You stole my watch and kept my keys,
My fair lady.

Off to prison she must go,
She must go, she must go;
Off to prison she must go,
My fair lady.

Take the key and lock her up,
Lock her up, lock her up;
Take the key and lock her up,
My fair lady.

PAT A CAKE

"Pat a cake, pat a cake,
Baker's man.
Make me a cake,
As fast as you can.
Pat it and prick it,
And mark it with a T,
And put it in the oven
For Tommy and me."

BOYS AND GIRLS, COME OUT TO PLAY

Boys and girls, come out to play,
The moon doth shine as bright as day,
Leave your supper and leave your sleep,
Come with your play-fellows into the street.
Come with a whoop, come with a call,
Come with a goodwill or not at all,
Up the ladder and down the wall,
A penny loaf will serve us all.
But when the loaf is gone, what will you do?
Those who would eat must work, that's true.

PEASE-PORRIDGE HOT

Pease-porridge hot,
Pease-porridge cold,
Pease-porridge in the pot, nine days old.

Spell me that without a p
And a clever scholar you will be.

DEEDLE, DEEDLE, DUMPLING, MY SON JOHN

Deedle, deedle, dumpling, my son John,
He went to bed with his stockings on,
One shoe off, and one shoe on,
Deedle, deedle, dumpling, my son John.

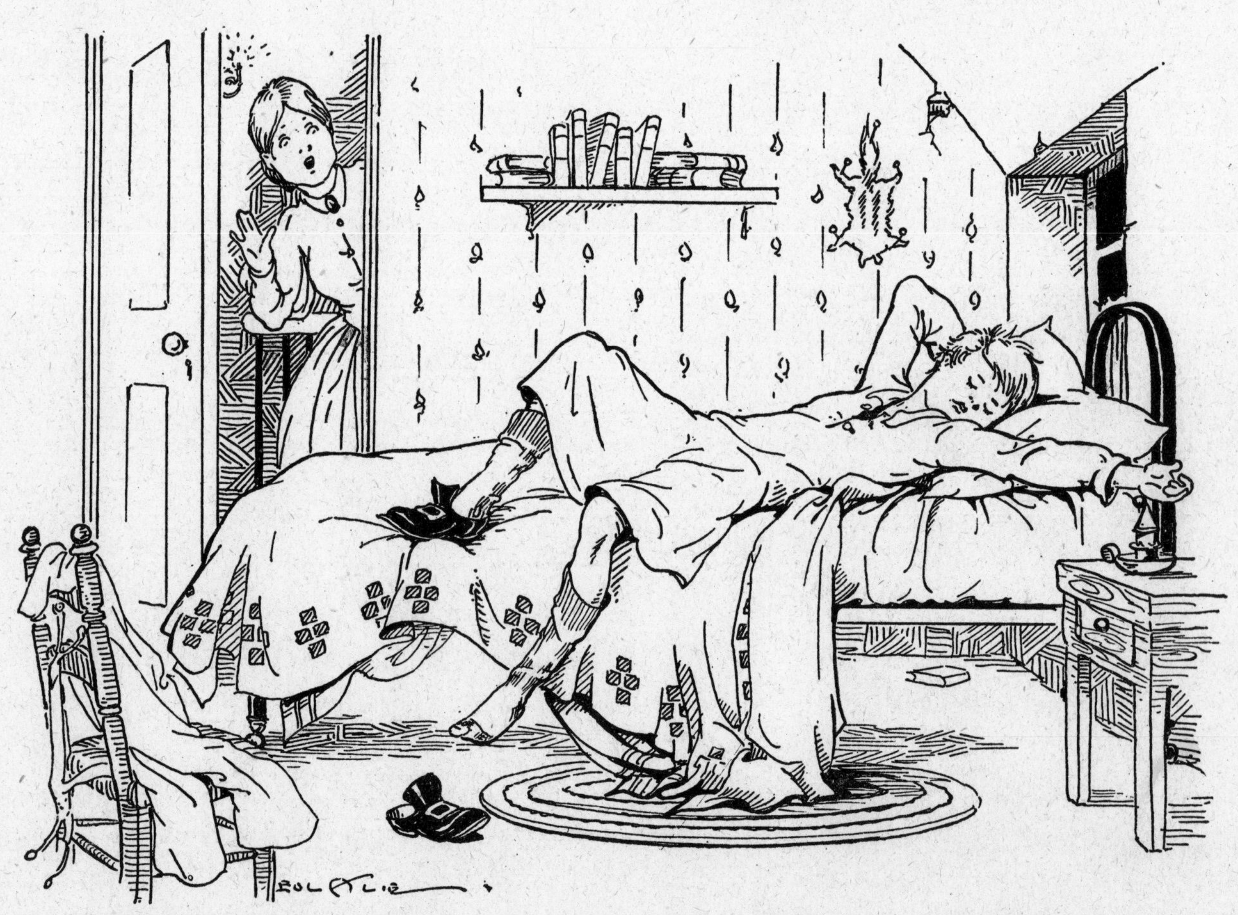

SUMMER BREEZE

Summer breeze, so softly blowing,
In my garden pinks are growing;
If you go and send the showers,
You may come and smell my
flowers.

LITTLE GIRL, LITTLE GIRL

"Little girl, little girl, where have
you been?"
"Gathering roses to give to the
Queen."
"Little girl, little girl, what gave
she you?"
"She gave me a diamond as big as
my shoe."

MARCH WINDS

March winds and April showers
Bring forth May flowers.

THANK YOU FOR THE EARTH SO SWEET

Thank You for the earth so sweet,
Thank You for the things we eat,
Thank You for the birds that sing,
Thank You, God, for everything.

HUSH-A-BYE

Hush-a-bye, baby, lie still with thy
daddy,
Thy mammy has gone to the mill,
To get some meal to bake a cake,
So pray, my dear baby, lie still.

JENNY WREN

Jenny Wren last week was wed,
And built her nest in grandpa's
shed;
Look next week and you shall see
Two little eggs, and maybe three.

MERRY ARE THE BELLS

Merry are the bells,
And merry would they ring,
Merry was myself,
And merry could I sing;
With a merry ding-dong,
Happy, gay, and free,
And a merry sing-song,
Happy let us be!

TWINKLE TWINKLE, LITTLE STAR

Twinkle, twinkle, little star,
How I wonder what you are!
Up above the world so high,
Like a diamond in the sky.

When the blazing sun is gone,
When he nothing shines upon,
Then you show your little light,
Twinkle, twinkle, all the night.

Then the traveler in the dark
Thanks you for your tiny spark:
How could he see where to go,
If you did not twinkle so?

In the dark blue sky you keep,
Often through my curtains peep,
For you never shut your eye,
Till the sun is in the sky.

As your bright and tiny spark
Lights the traveler in the dark,
Though I know not what you are,
Twinkle, twinkle, little star.

TWO LITTLE BEAVERS

Two little beavers lived in a dam,
One named Sue, the other named Sam.
Come to me, Sue; come to me, Sam;
Go again, Sue; go again, Sam.

MISTRESS MARY, QUITE CONTRARY

Mistress Mary,
Quite contrary,
How does your garden grow?
With silver bells,
And cockleshells,
And pretty maids all in a row.

UP THE LADDER

Up the ladder and down the wall,
A halfpenny roll will serve us all.
You find milk, and I'll find flour,
And we'll have a pudding in half an hour.

THERE WAS AN OLD MAN

There was an old man,
And he had a calf,
And that's half;
He took him out of the stall
And put him on the wall,
And that's all.

OH, RARE HARRY PARRY

Oh, rare Harry Parry,
When will you marry?
When apples and pears are ripe,
I'll come to your wedding,
Without any bidding,
And dance and sing all the night.

LITTLE JACK HORNER

Little Jack Horner
Sat in a corner,
Eating of Christmas pie;
He put in his thumb,
And pulled out a plum,
And cried, "What a good boy
am I!"

THUMBIKIN, THUMBIKIN

Thumbikin, Thumbikin, broke the
barn;
Pinnikin, Pinnikin, stole the corn;
Long-back'd Gray
Carried it away;
Old Mid-man sat and saw;
But Peesy-weesy paid and a'.

This broke the barn;
This stole the corn;
This got none;
This went pinky-winky
All the way home.

MOLLY, MY SISTER, AND I FELL OUT

Molly, my sister, and I fell out,
And what do you think it was all
about?
She loved coffee and I loved tea,
And that was the reason we
couldn't agree.

I HAD A LITTLE NUT-TREE

I had a little nut-tree, nothing
  would it bear
But a silver nutmeg and a golden
  pear;
The King of Spain's daughter came
  to visit me,
And all was because of my little
  nut-tree.
I skipped over water, I danced
  over sea,
And all the birds in the air couldn't
  catch me.

OH, WHERE, OH, WHERE IS MY LITTLE DOG GONE?

Oh, where, oh, where is my little
  dog gone?
  Oh, where, oh, where can he be?
With his ears cut short and his tail
  cut long,
  Oh, where, oh, where is he?

BESSY BELL AND MARY GRAY

Bessy Bell and Mary Gray,
  They were two bonnie lasses:
They built a house upon the lea,
  And covered it with rushes.
Bessy kept the garden gate,
  And Mary kept the pantry:
Bessy always had to wait,
  While Mary lived in plenty.

JACK SPRAT

Jack Sprat could eat no fat,
  His wife could eat no lean;
And so betwixt them both, you see,
  They licked the platter clean.

WHEN I WAS A LITTLE BOY

When I was a little boy
  I had but little wit;
'Tis a long time ago,
  And I have no more yet,
Nor ever, ever shall
  Until that I die,
For the longer I live
  The more fool am I.

PEMMY WAS A PRETTY GIRL

Pemmy was a pretty girl,
  But Fanny was a better;
Pemmy looked like any churl,
  When little Fanny let her.

Pemmy had a pretty nose,
  But Fanny had a better;
Pemmy oft would come to blows,
  But Fanny would not let her.

Pemmy had a pretty doll,
  But Fanny had a better;
Pemmy chatter'd like a poll,
  When little Fanny let her.

Pemmy had a pretty song,
  But Fanny had a better;
Pemmy would sing all day long,
  But Fanny would not let her.

Pemmy lov'd a pretty lad,
  And Fanny lov'd a better;
And Pemmy wanted for to wed,
  But Fanny would not let her.

DIDDLEDY, DIDDLEDY, DUMPTY

Diddledy, diddledy, dumpty:
The cat ran up the plum-tree.
  I'll lay you a crown
  I'll fetch you down;
So diddledy, diddledy, dumpty.

TOM, HE WAS A PIPER'S SON

PETER PIPER

Peter Piper picked a peck of pickled pepper;
A peck of pickled pepper Peter Piper picked;
If Peter Piper picked a peck of pickled pepper,
Where's the peck of pickled pepper Peter Piper picked?

THERE WAS A LITTLE WOMAN

There was a little woman, as I've been told,
Who was not very young, nor yet very old,
Now this little woman her living got,
By selling mince pies, hot, hot, hot!

TOM, HE WAS A PIPER'S SON

Tom, he was a piper's son,
He learnt to play when he was young,
But all the tune that he could play
Was "Over the hills and far away."

Over the hills, and a great way off,
And the wind will blow my top-knot off.

Tom with his pipe made such a noise,
That he pleased both the girls and boys;
And they all stopped to hear him play,
"Over the hills and far away."

Tom with his pipe did play with such skill
That those who heard him could never keep still;
As soon as he played they began to dance,
Even pigs on their hind legs would after him prance.

LITTLE WIND

Little wind, blow on the hill top;
Little wind, blow down the plain;
Little wind, blow up the sunshine;
Little wind, blow off the rain.

PRAY WHICH IS THE WAY TO LONDON TOWN?

Pray, which is the way to London Town?
I must be there to-night.
O, walk a hundred miles and turn
To left and then to right;
Then straight as a line and then zig-zag,
Then uphill and then down,
Walk quick and in six months you'll be
Not far from London Town.

THREE BLIND MICE

Three blind mice, see how they run!
They all ran after the farmer's wife,
Who cut off their tails with the carving-knife,
Did you ever see such a thing in your life?
As three blind mice.

THERE WAS AN OLD WOMAN

There was an old woman who lived in a shoe,
She had so many children she didn't know what to do;
She gave them some broth without any bread,
And whipped them all well, and put them to bed.

I HAD A LITTLE COW

I had a little cow; to save her,
I turned her into the meadow to graze her:
There came a heavy storm of rain,
And drove the little cow home again.
The church doors they stood open,
And there the little cow was cropen;
The bell-ropes they were made of hay,
And the little cow ate them all away:
The sexton came to toll the bell,
And pushed the little cow into the well!

DANCE, LITTLE BABY, DANCE UP HIGH!

Dance, little baby, dance up high!
Never mind, Baby, Mother is by.
Crow and caper, caper and crow,
There, little Baby, there you go!
Up to the ceiling, down to the ground,
Backwards and forwards, round and round.
Dance, little Baby, and Mother will sing
With a merry carol, ding! ding! ding!

BRING THE HOOP

Bring the hoop, and bring the ball,
Come with happy faces all;
Let us make a merry ring,
Talk and laugh, and dance and sing;
Quickly, quickly, come away,
For it is a pleasant day.

BROW BRINKY

Brow brinky,
Eye kinky,
Chin choppy,
Nose noppy,
Cheek cherry,
Mouth merry.

BEES

A swarm of bees in May
Is worth a load of hay;
A swarm of bees in June
Is worth a silver spoon;
A swarm of bees in July
Is not worth a fly.

RIDE AWAY, RIDE AWAY

Ride away, ride away,
Johnny shall ride,
And he shall have pussy-cat
Tied to one side;
He shall have little dog
Tied to the other,
And Johnny shall ride
To see his grandmother.

PETER, PETER, PUMPKIN EATER

LITTLE BOY BLUE

Little Boy Blue, come, blow your horn,
The cow's in the meadow, the sheep's in the corn;
But where is the little boy tending the sheep?
He's under the haystack fast asleep.
Will you wake him? No, not I!
For if I do, he's sure to cry.

EARLY TO BED

Early to bed, Early to rise.
Makes a man healthy, wealthy and wise.

PETER, PETER, PUMPKIN-EATER

Peter, Peter, pumpkin-eater,
Had a wife, and couldn't keep her;
He put her in a pumpkin shell,
And there he kept her very well.

Peter, Peter, pumpkin-eater
Had another and didn't love her;
Peter learned to read and spell,
And then he loved her very well.

BLACK WITHIN

Black within, and red without:
Four corners round about.
(A chimney)

LITTLE MAID, PRETTY MAID

Little maid, pretty maid, whither goest thou?
"Down in the meadow to milk my cow."
Shall I go with thee? "No, not now;
When I send for thee, then come thou."

FOR BABY

You shall have an apple,
You shall have a plum,
You shall have a rattle,
When papa comes home.

HOW MANY MILES IS IT TO BABYLON?

How many miles is it to Babylon?
  Threescore miles and ten.
Can I get there by candle-light?
Yes, and back again!
If your heels are nimble and light,
You may get there by candle-light.

AH! HEAR THE WIND BLOW!

Ah! hear the wind blow!
And see the deep snow!
Where now are the birds we love
  to hear sing?
They are where it's warm,
They are free of all harm.
They will come back again in the
  spring, in the spring.

TO MARKET, TO MARKET

To market, to market, a gallop, a
  trot,
To buy some meat to put in the
  pot;
Five cents a quarter, ten cents a
  side,
If it hadn't been killed, it must
  have died.

BABY, MY DOLLY

Baby, my dolly, oh, she never cries!
Lie still, my darling, and close
  your little eyes!
Mother must go, dear, and look for
  the others—
All the dear sisters, and all the
  dear brothers.

A LITTLE OLD MAN OF DERBY

A little old man of Derby,
  How do you think he served me?
He took away my bread and
    cheese,
  And that is how he served me.

DARBY AND JOAN WERE DRESSED IN BLACK

Darby and Joan were dressed in
  black,
Sword and buckle behind their
  back;
Foot for foot, and knee for knee,
Turn about, Darby's company!

BIRCH AND GREEN HOLLY

Birch and green holly, boys,
  Birch and green holly;
If you get beaten, boys,
  'Twill be your own folly.

LITTLE DROPS OF WATER

Little drops of water,
  Little grains of sand,
Make the mighty ocean,
  And the pleasant land.

THE OLD WOMAN FROM FRANCE

There came an old woman from
  France
Who taught grown-up children to
  dance;
But they were so stiff,
She sent them home in a sniff,
This sprightly old woman from
  France.

THERE'S A NEAT LITTLE CLOCK

There's a neat little clock—
In the schoolroom it stands—
And it points to the time
With its two little hands.

And may we, like the clock,
Keep a face clean and bright,
With hands ever ready
To do what is right.

THIRTY DAYS HATH SEPTEMBER

Thirty days hath September,
April, June, and November;
February has twenty-eight alone,
All the rest have thirty-one;
But Leap Year coming once in four.
February then has one day more.

COCK CROWS IN THE MORN

Cock crows in the morn to tell us to rise,
And he who lies late will never be wise;
For early to bed, and early to rise,
Is the way to be healthy and wealthy and wise.

WASN'T IT FUNNY?

Wasn't it funny? hear it, all people!
Little Tom Thumb has swallowed
a steeple!

How did he do it?
I'll tell you, my son!
'Twas made of white sugar—and
easily done!

HIPPETY HOP TO THE BARBER SHOP

Hippety hop to the barber shop,
To get a stick of candy,
One for you and one for me,
And one for Sister Mandy.

THERE WAS AN OLD WOMAN

There was an old woman of Leeds,
Who spent all her time in good
deeds;
She worked for the poor
Till her fingers were sore,
This pious old woman of Leeds!

UP STREET, AND DOWN STREET

Up street, and down street,
Each window is made of glass;
If you go to Tommy Tickler's
house,
You'll find a pretty lass.

SEE-SAW, MARGERY DAW

See-saw, Margery Daw,
Jacky shall have a new master;
Jacky must have but a penny a
day,
Because he can work no faster.

PUSSY SITS BEHIND THE LOG

Pussy sits behind the log,
How can she be fair?
Then comes in the little dog,
"Pussy, are you there?
So, so, dear Mistress Pussy,
Pray tell me how do you do?"
"I thank you, little Doggie,
I fare as well as you."

Every piper he had a fine pipe,
And a very fine pipe had he.
Then tootle, tootle-too, tootle-too went the pipers,
Twang, twang-a-twang, twang-a-twang went the harpers,
Twee, tweedle-dee, tweedle-dee went the fiddlers.
Oh, there's none so rare as can compare
With King Cole and his pipers three!

Old King Cole was a merry old soul,
And a merry old soul was he;
He called for his pipe, and he called for his bowl,
And he called for his drummers three.
Every drummer he had a fine drum,
And a very fine drum had he.
Then rub-a-dub, a-dub, rub-a-dub went the drummers,
Tootle, tootle - too, tootle - too went the pipers,
Twang, twang-a-twang, twang-a-twang went the harpers,
Twee, tweedle-dee, tweedle-dee went the fiddlers.
Oh, there's none so rare as can compare
With King Cole and his drummers three!

He called for his pipe, and he called
for his bowl,
And he called for his fiddlers three.
Every fiddler he had a fiddle,
And a very fine fiddle had he;
Twee, tweedle-dee, tweedle-dee
went the fiddlers.
Oh, there's none so rare as can
compare
With King Cole and his fiddlers
three!

Old King Cole was a merry old
soul,
And a merry old soul was he;
He called for his pipe, and he called
for his bowl,
And he called for his harpers three.

Every harper he had a fine harp,
And a very fine harp had he.
Twang, twan-a-twang went the
harpers,
Twee, tweedle-dee, tweedle-dee
went the fiddlers.
Oh, there's none so rare as can
compare
With King Cole and his harpers
three!

Old King Cole was a merry old
soul,
And a merry old soul was he;
He called for his pipe, and he called
for his bowl,
And he called for his pipers three.

OLD KING COLE

HUSH-A-BY, BABY

Hush-a-by, baby, on the tree top,
When the wind blows, the cradle
 will rock,
When the bough bends, the cradle
 will fall,
Down will come baby, bough, cradle, and all.

I LIKE LITTLE PUSSY

I like little pussy, her coat is so
 warm,
And if I don't hurt her she'll do me
 no harm;
So I'll not pull her tail, nor drive
 her away,
But pussy and I very gently will
 play.

OLD KING COLE

Old King Cole was a merry old
 soul,
And a merry old soul was he;

WHO'S THAT RINGING AT OUR FRONT DOOR BELL?

Who's that ringing at our front door bell?
I'm a little pussy cat and I'm not very well.
Then put your little nose in a little mutton fat,
And that's the way to cure a little pussy cat.

HOW DO YOU DO, NEIGHBOR?

How do you do, neighbor?
Neighbor, how do you do?
Very well, I thank you.
How does Cousin Sue do?
She is very well,
And sends her love to you,
And so does Cousin Bell.
Ah! how, pray, does she do?

HARK, HARK, THE DOGS DO BARK!

Hark, hark, the dogs do bark!
Beggars are coming to town,
Some in rags, some in tags,
And some in velvet gown.

HICKETY PICKETY, MY BLACK HEN

Hickety Pickety, my black hen,
She lays eggs for gentlemen;
Sometimes nine, and sometimes
ten,
Hickety Pickety, my fat hen.

AS I WAS GOING UP PIPPEN HILL

As I was going up Pippen Hill,—
Pippen Hill was dirty,—
There I met a pretty miss,
And she dropped me a curtesy.

Little miss, pretty miss,
Blessings light upon you!
If I had half-a-crown a day,
I'd spend it all upon you.

TO MARKET, TO MARKET

To market, to market,
To buy a penny bun,
Home again, home again,
Market is done.

SPEAK WHEN YOU'RE SPOKEN TO

Speak when you're spoken to,
Come when once called;
Shut the door after you,
And turn to the wall!

TWO LITTLE DOGS

Two little dogs
Sat by the fire,
Over a fender of coal-dust;
Said one little dog
To the other little dog,
If you don't talk, why, I must.

IF YOU ARE TO BE A GENTLEMAN

If you are to be a gentleman,
As I suppose you'll be,
You'll neither laugh nor smile
For a tickling of the knee.

I'LL SING YOU A SONG

I'll sing you a song,
Though not very long,
Yet I think it's as pretty as any;
Put your hand in your purse,
You'll never be worse,
And give the poor singer a penny.

OLD MOTHER HUBBARD

OLD MOTHER HUBBARD

Old Mother Hubbard,
Went to the cupboard,
To get her poor Dog a bone,

But when she got there,
The cupboard was bare,
And so the poor Dog had none.

She went to the Baker's
To buy him some bread,
And when she came back
The dog stood on his head.

She went to the Hatter's
To buy him a hat,
And when she came back,
He was feeding the cat.

She took a clean dish
To get him some tripe,
And when she came back
He was smoking a pipe.

She went to the Fishmonger's
To buy him some fish,
And when she came back
He was licking the dish.

She went to the Tailor's
To buy him a coat,
And when she came back
He was riding the goat.

She went to the Barber's
To buy him a wig,
And when she came back
He was dancing a jig.

The dame made a curtsy,
The dog made a bow,
The dame said, "Your Servant;"
The dog said, "Bow-wow."

RING-A-RING-A-ROSES

Ring-a-ring-a-roses,
A pocket full of posies;
Hush! Hush! Hush!
We'll all tumble down.

HERE'S SULKY SUE

Here's Sulky Sue,
What shall we do?
Turn her face to the wall
Till she comes to.

I LOVE YOU WELL

I love you well, my little
    brother,
  And you are fond of me;
Let us be kind to one an-
    other,
  As brothers ought to be.
You shall learn to play with
    me,
  And learn to use my toys;
And then I think that we
    shall be
  Two happy little boys.

SATURDAY, SUNDAY

On Saturday night
It shall be my care
To powder my locks
And curl my hair.

On Sunday morning
My love will come in,
When he will marry me
With a gold ring.

BRYAN O'LIN

Bryan O'Lin had no breeches to
  wear
So he bought him a sheepskin and
  made him a pair.

With the skinny side out, and the
  woolly side in,
"Ah, ha, that is warm!" said Bryan
  O'Lin.

THREE WISE MEN OF GOTHAM

Three wise men of Gotham
They went to sea in a bowl,
And if the bowl had been stronger
My song had been longer.

AS I WAS GOING ALONG

As I was going along, long, long,
A-singing a comical song, song, song.
The lane that I went was so long, long, long,
And the song that I sung was so long, long, long,
And so I went singing along.

I HAVE A LITTLE SISTER

I have a little sister, they call her Peep, Peep;
She wades the waters deep, deep, deep;
She climbs the mountains high, high, high;
Poor little creature, she has but one eye!

(*A Star*)

BIRDS OF A FEATHER

Birds of a feather flock together,
And so will pigs and swine;
Rats and mice will have their choice,
And so will I have mine.

THE QUEEN OF HEARTS

The Queen of Hearts
She made some tarts,
All on a summer's day,
The Knave of Hearts
He stole those tarts,
And took them clean away.

The King of Hearts
Called for the tarts,
And beat the Knave full sore;
The Knave of Hearts
Brought back the tarts,
And vowed he'd steal no more.

IF I WERE AN APPLE

If I were an apple
  And grew on a tree,
I think I'd drop down
  On a nice boy like me.

I wouldn't stay there
  Giving nobody joy;
I'd fall down at once
  And say, "Eat me, my boy!"

SLEEP, BABY, SLEEP

  Sleep, baby, sleep,
Our cottage vale is deep,
The little lamb is on the green,
With woolly fleece so soft and clean.
  Sleep, baby, sleep.

  Sleep, baby, sleep.
Down where the woodbines creep;
Be always like the lamb so mild,
A kind and sweet and gentle child.
  Sleep, baby, sleep.

THE ROSE IS RED

The rose is red, the violet's blue;
Honey's sweet; so are you.

COME HITHER, SWEET ROBIN

Come hither, sweet robin,
And be not afraid,
I would not hurt even a feather;
Come hither, sweet robin,
And pick up some bread,
To feed you this very cold weather.

DAFFY-DOWN-DILLY

Daffy-down-dilly has come up to town,
In a yellow petticoat and a green gown.

ELSIE MARLEY

Elsie Marley is grown so fine
She won't get up to feed the swine,
But lies in bed till eight or nine,
And surely she does take her time.

Do you ken Elsie Marley, honey?
The wife who sells the barley, honey?
She won't get up to feed her swine,
And do you ken Elsie Marley, honey?

A RED SKY IN THE MORNING

A red sky in the morning
Is the shepherd's warning,
A red sky at night
Is the shepherd's delight.

GOD BLESS THE MASTER

God bless the master of this house,
Likewise the mistress too,
And all the little children
That round the table go;

And all your kin and kinsmen,
That dwell both far and near;
I wish you a Merry Christmas,
And a Happy New Year.

CHRISTMAS IS COMING

Christmas is coming, the geese are getting fat;
Please put a penny in the old man's hat.

THE FAIR MAID WHO, THE FIRST OF MAY

The fair maid who, the first of May,
Goes to the fields at break of day,
And washes in dew from the hawthorn tree,
Will ever after handsome be.

CURLY LOCKS! CURLY LOCKS!

Curly locks! Curly locks! wilt thou
be mine?
Thou shalt not wash dishes, nor
yet feed the swine;
But sit on a cushion and sew a fine
seam,
And feed upon strawberries, sugar,
and cream.

OLD WOMAN, OLD WOMAN

Old woman, old woman, shall we
go a-shearing?
Speak a little louder, sir—I am
very thick of hearing.
Old woman, old woman, shall I
love you dearly?
Thank you, kind sir. I hear you
very clearly.

HOW MANY DAYS HAS MY BABY TO PLAY?

How many days has my baby to
play?
Saturday, Sunday, Monday,
Tuesday, Wednesday, Thursday,
Friday,
Saturday, Sunday, Monday.

THREE CHILDREN SLIDING ON THE ICE

Three children sliding on the ice
  Upon a summer's day,
As it fell out they all fell in,
  The rest they ran away.

Oh, had these children been at school
  Or sliding on dry ground,
Ten thousand pounds to one penny
  They had not then been drowned.

You parents that have children dear,
  And eke you that have none,
If you would keep them safe abroad,
  Pray keep them all at home.

ONE, TWO, THREE, FOUR, FIVE

One, two, three, four, five,
I caught a fish alive.
Why did you let it go?—
Because it bit my finger so.

THERE WAS A LITTLE GIRL

There was a little girl, and she wore a little curl
Right down the middle of her forehead;
When she was good, she was very, very good,
But when she was bad she was horrid.

One day she went upstairs, while her parents, unawares,
In the kitchen down below were occupied with meals;
And she stood upon her head, on her little truckle-bed,
And she then began hurray-ing with her heels.

Her mother heard the noise, and thought it was the boys
A-playing at a combat in the attic;
But when she climbed the stair, and saw Jemima there,
She took and she did whip her most emphatic.

HUMPTY-DUMPTY

Humpty-Dumpty sat on a
  wall,
Humpty-Dumpty had a
  great fall;
All the King's horses, and
  all the King's men,
Could not put Humpty-
  Dumpty together again.

MIND YOUR COMMAS

Every lady in this land
Has twenty nails, upon each hand
Five, and twenty on hands and
  feet,
All this is true, without deceit.

I'LL TELL YOU A STORY

I'll tell you a story
About Jack of Nory
And now my story's begun,
I'll tell you another
About his brother,
And now my story is done.

HERE WE GO

Here we go up, up, up,
Here we go down, down, down,
Here we go backward and forward,
And here we go round, round,
  round.

LITTLE MAIDEN

Little maiden,
Better tarry;
Time enough next year to marry.
Hearts may change,
And so may fancy;
Wait a little longer, Nancy.

INDEX TO FIRST LINES

j
Mo

94132

Copyright, 1922, 1927, 1931 and 1932
By
THE PLATT & MUNK CO., Inc.

MADE IN U. S. A.

AQUINAS COLLEGE LIBRARY
Grand Rapids, Mich.

MOTHER GOOSE RHYMES

EDITED BY
WATTY PIPER

Illustrations by
EULALIE and LOIS L. LENSKI

·NEW·YORK·
·THE·PLATT·&·MUNK·CO INC·

SING A SONG OF SIXPENCE